Mighty Mighty **MONSTERS**

NEW
MONSTER
in SCHOOL

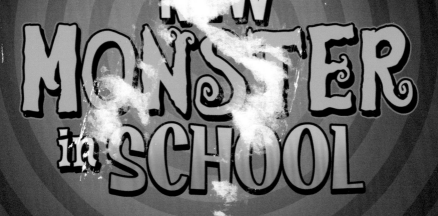

created by Sean O'Reilly
illustrated by Arcana Studio

Raintree

www.raintreepublishers.co.uk
Visit our website to find out
more information about
Raintree books.

To order:
☎ Phone 0845 6044371
▤ Fax +44 (0) 1865 312263
✉ Email myorders@raintreepublishers.co.uk

Customers from outside the UK please telephone +44 1865 312262

Raintree is an imprint of Capstone Global Library Limited,
a company incorporated in England and Wales having its registered
office at 7 Pilgrim Street, London, EC4V 6LB
– Registered company number: 6695582

First published by Stone Arch Books in 2010
First published in the United Kingdom in paperback in 2012
The moral rights of the proprietor have been asserted.

Edited by Laura Knowles
Originated by Capstone Global Library Ltd
Printed and bound in China by South China Printing Company

ISBN 978 1 406 23723 8 (paperback)
16 15 14 13 12
10 9 8 7 6 5 4 3 2 1

British Library Cataloguing in Publication Data
A full catalogue record for this book is available
from the British Library.

In a strange corner of the world known as Transylmania . . .

Legendary monsters were born.

WELCOME TO TRANSYLMANIA

But long before their frightful fame, these classic creatures faced fears of their own.

To take on terrifying teachers and homework horrors, they formed the most fearsome friendship on Earth . . .

Mighty Mighty MONSTERS

Vlad

Talbot

Witchita

Milton

Poto

Frankie

Igor

Mary

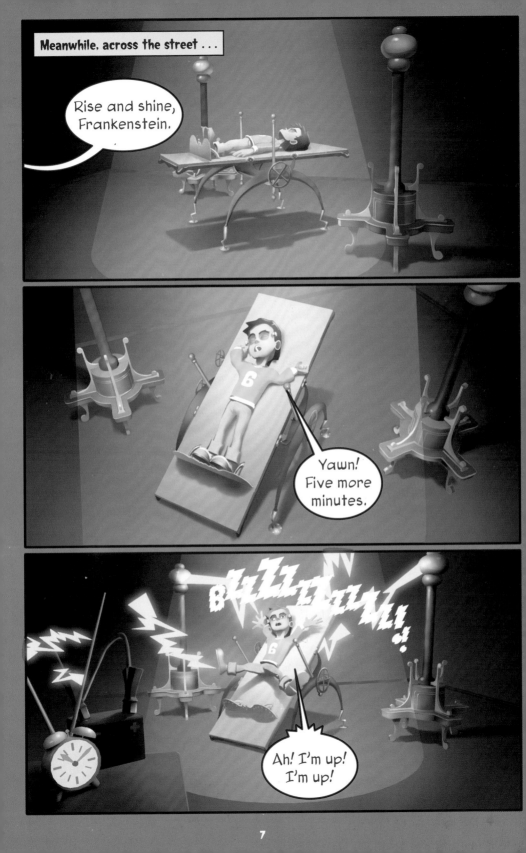

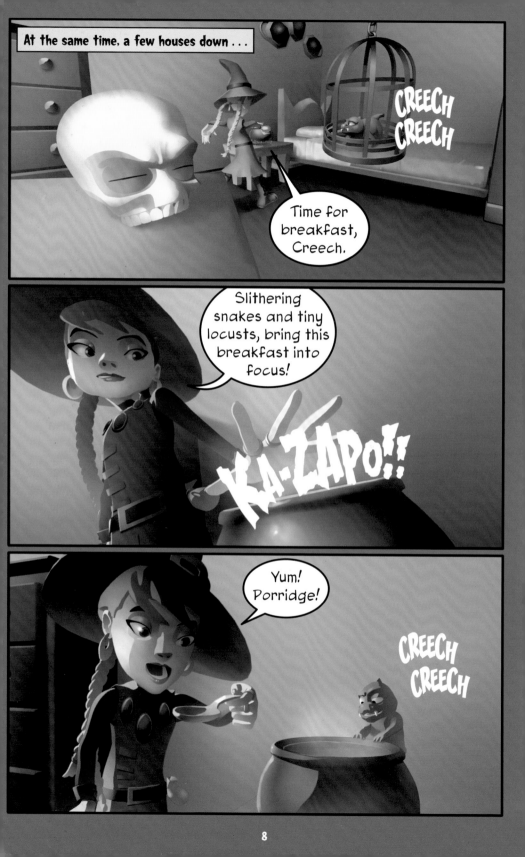

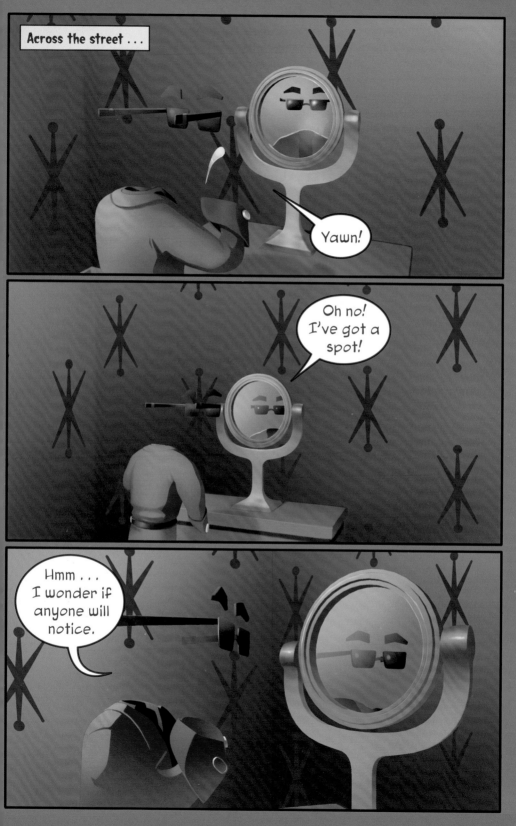

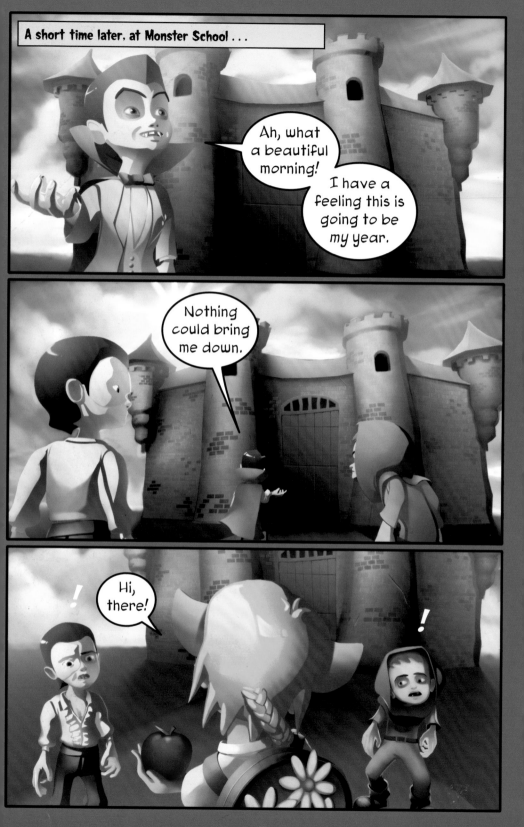

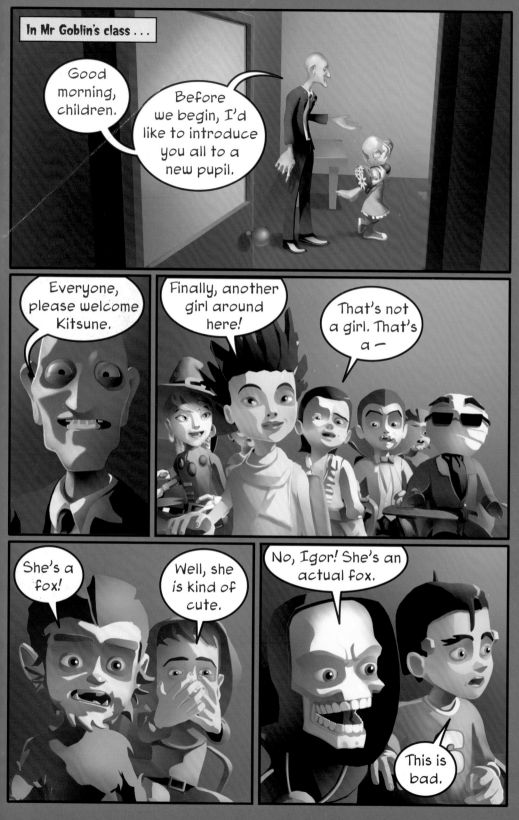

22

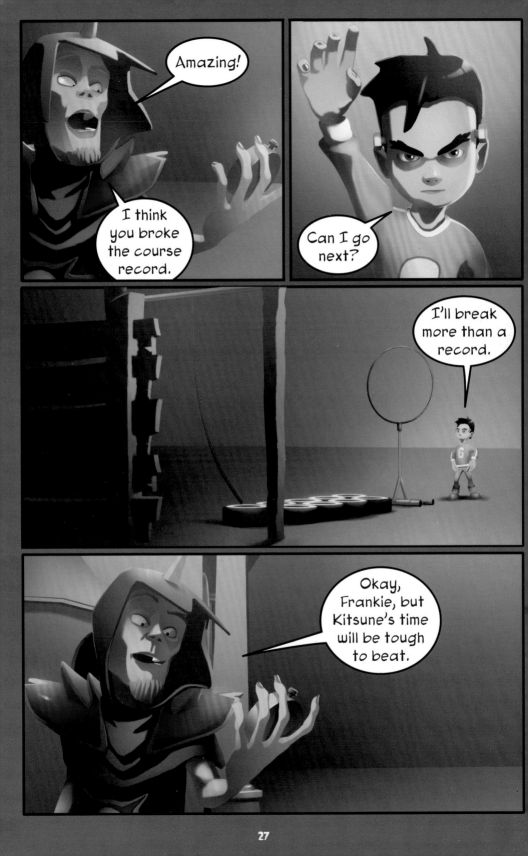

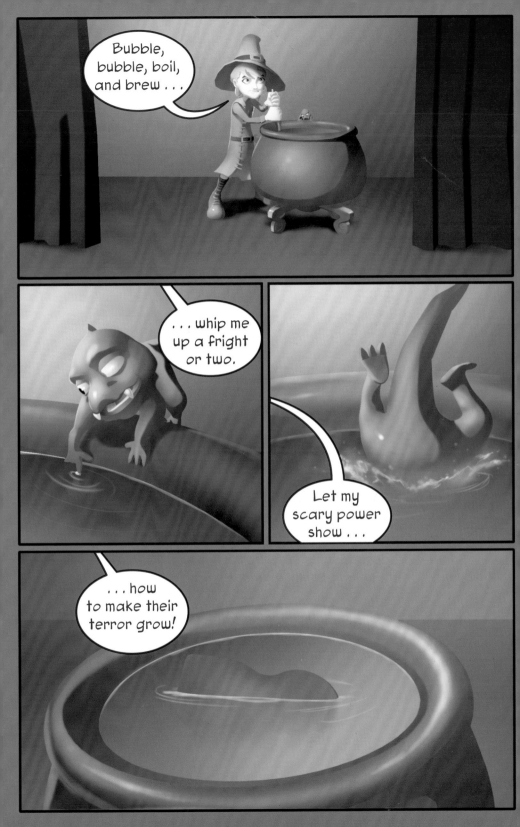

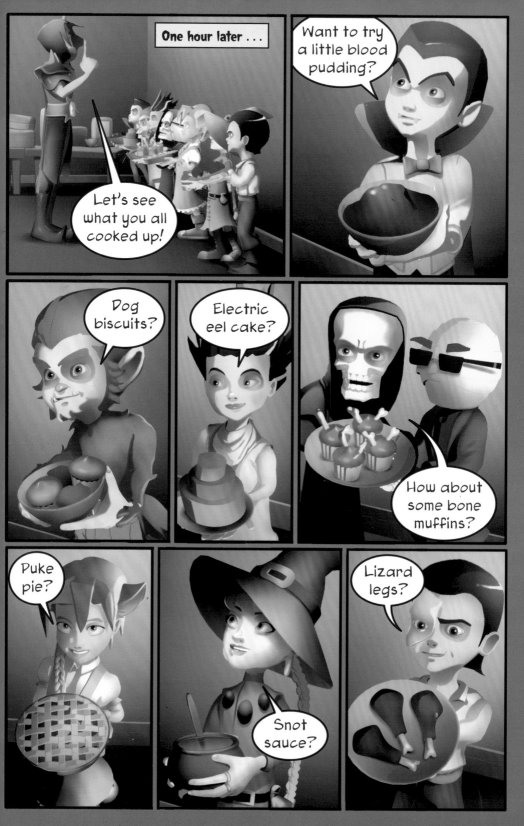

36

SPOOKY
FOREST

MONSTER
SCHOOL

FLAME OF
HALLOWEEN

CASTLE OF
DOOM

Mighty Mighty
MONSTERS

...BEFORE THEY WERE STARS!

KITSUNE

Nickname: Kit

Hometown: Tokyo, Japan

Favourite colour: pink

Favourite animal: foxes (of course!)

Mighty mighty powers: superhuman quickness on her feet; cleverness; extraordinary leaping ability; super friendliness.

BIOGRAPHY

Kitsune didn't grow up in Transylmania, but she quickly became an important member of the Mighty Mighty Monsters. Her speed and cleverness are unmatched. With her love for all things pink, she also adds a dose of "girl power" to the ghoulish gang. Although this fantastic fox is already a legend in her home country of Japan, she has made an instant impact on her new home.

In the country of Japan, *Kitsune* means fox. These clever animals have appeared in Japanese folklore for thousands of years.

In many folk tales, Kitsune creatures have magical powers and super intelligence. They can also have as many as nine tails. These tails show a Kitsune's age. A young fox might only have one, but an old fox could have many more.

Kitsune are famous for their cleverness. Often, they cannot be trusted and are considered greedy tricksters.

About Sean O'Reilly
and Arcana Studio

As a lifelong comics fan, Sean O'Reilly dreamed of becoming a comic book creator. In 2004, he realized that dream by creating Arcana Studio. In one short year, O'Reilly took his studio from a one-person operation in his house to an award-winning comic book publisher with more than 150 graphic novels produced for Harper Collins, Simon & Schuster, Random House, Scholastic, and others.

Within a year, the company won many awards including the Shuster Award for Outstanding Publisher and the Moonbeam Award for top children's graphic novel. O'Reilly also won the Top 40 Under 40 award from the city of Vancouver and authored *The Clockwork Girl* for Top Graphic Novel at Book Expo America in 2009.

Currently, O'Reilly is one of the most prolific independent comic book writers in Canada. While showing no signs of slowing down in comics, he now also writes screenplays and adapts his creations for the big screen.

Glossary

batty crazy or insane

competition contest of some kind

destroyed wrecked or ruined

fearsome frightening, such as a monster

focus make something clearer to see with your eyes

introduce tell the name of one person to another person

Kitsune Japanese word for fox, an animal often found in that country's folklore

locust type of grasshopper that eats and destroys crops

obstacle training course, which usually has fences, walls, and ditches to climb over or get around

terror person or thing that causes very great fear

DISCUSSION QUESTIONS

1. Why do you think the boy monsters didn't like Kitsune at first? Do you think they liked her at the end of the story? Explain.

2. Who do you think deserves the Mon-Star Award? Choose one monster and explain why he or she is the scariest.

3. All of the Mighty Mighty Monsters are different. Which character do you like the best and why?

WRITING PROMPTS

1. Have you ever been in a competition? Did you win or lose? Write a story about the game or event.

2. Write a story about your own group of friends. What kind of adventures do you have? What do you do for fun?

3. Write your own Mighty Mighty Monsters adventure. What will the ghoulish gang do next? What villains will they face? You decide.

FIND OUT MORE

INFORMATION BOOKS

The Mystery of Vampires and Werewolves (Can Science Solve?), Chris Oxlade (Heinemann Library, 2008)

Vampires and the Undead (Dark Side), Anita Ganeri (Wayland, 2010)

GRAPHIC NOVELS

Dracula (Graphic Revolve), Bram Stoker, retold by Michael Burgan (Raintree, 2009)

Frankenstein (Graphic Revolve), Mary Shelley, retold by Michael Burgan (Raintree, 2009)

The Invisible Man (Graphic Chillers), H. G. Wells, retold by Joeming Dunn (Franklin Watts, 2010)

WEBSITE

learnenglishkids.britishcouncil.org/en/make-your-own/make-your-monster
Visit this website to create your own monster. You can also invent your own scary story, dangerous animal, or superhero.

Mighty Mighty MONSTERS ADVENTURES

Monster Mansion
ISBN: 978 1 406 23721 4

My Missing Monster
ISBN: 978 1 406 23722 1

Hide and Shriek
ISBN: 978 1 406 23718 4

The King of Halloween Castle
ISBN: 978 1 406 23719 1

Lost in Spooky Forest
ISBN: 978 1 406 23720 7